2

WHO ARE THE
REBELS?

© & TM 2014 Lucasfilm Ltd.

Printed in China
First Edition, December 2014
1 3 5 7 9 10 8 6 4 2

ISBN 978-1-4847-2607-5
T425-2382-5-14356

Visit the official *Star Wars* website at: www.starwars.com
This book was printed   paper created from a sustainable source.

Disney
LUCASFILM
PRESS

Los Angeles • New York

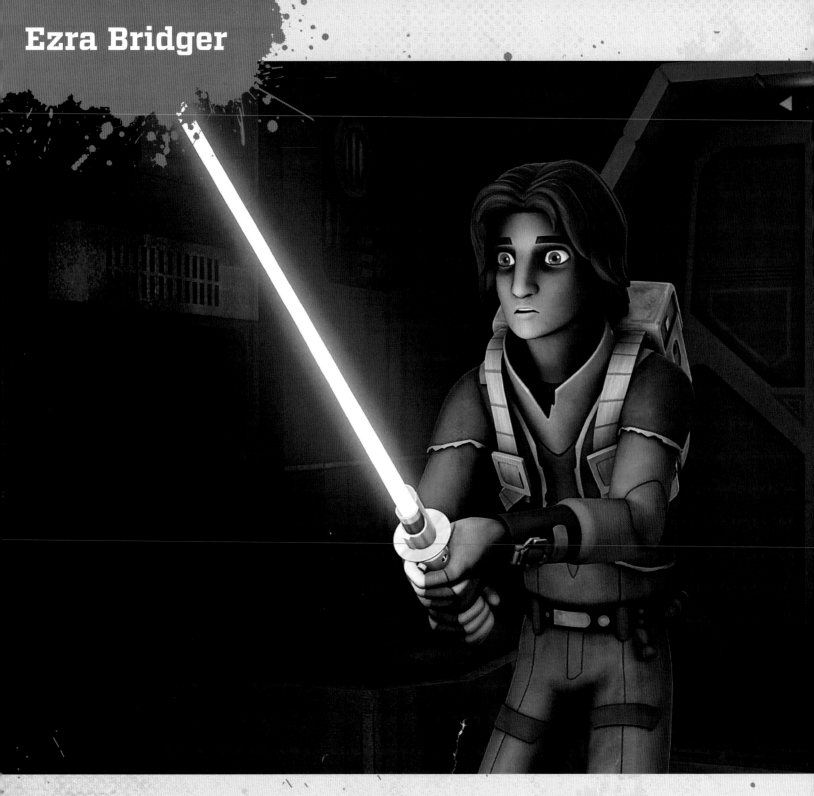

Ezra Bridger

Ezra holds Kanan's lightsaber for the first time.

Ezra Bridger isn't your average fourteen-year-old kid. Growing up alone on the streets of Lothal has taught him how to take care of himself.

When Ezra meets Kanan Jarrus and his band of rebels, he discovers that his quick reflexes are a result of his connection to the Force. Kanan offers to train Ezra in the ways of the Jedi Order. While Ezra isn't always the most patient student, he is eager to learn and greatly admires Kanan's abilities. Confident, clever, and ready to take the fight to the Empire, Ezra is a perfect addition to the rebel team.

Kanan Jarrus is a Jedi Knight and the apparent leader of the rebels—a dangerous combination. After all, the Empire has dedicated itself to hunting down all Jedi and destroying them. Because of this, Kanan often has to hide his abilities and his lightsaber.

Kanan was recruited to the rebel cause by Hera Syndulla, and the two have been close ever since. Together, they have planned and pulled off many missions that will help overthrow the evil Empire. Kanan's strategic thinking and deadly combat skills make him a fearsome warrior and a great leader.

Kanan draws his lightsaber to protect the rebels.

Garazeb "Zeb" Orrelios

Watch out for Zeb!

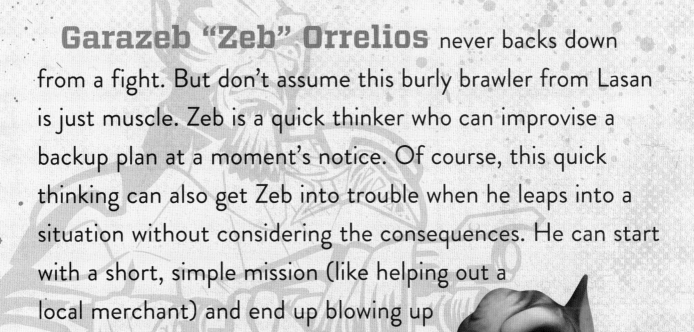

Garazeb "Zeb" Orrelios never backs down from a fight. But don't assume this burly brawler from Lasan is just muscle. Zeb is a quick thinker who can improvise a backup plan at a moment's notice. Of course, this quick thinking can also get Zeb into trouble when he leaps into a situation without considering the consequences. He can start with a short, simple mission (like helping out a local merchant) and end up blowing up a TIE fighter and half a city block!

Zeb's weapon of choice is a bo-rifle, although he also enjoys banging stormtroopers' heads together. When the rebels find themselves backed into a corner, there's no one they'd rather have by their side than Zeb.

As captain of the *Ghost*, **Hera Syndulla** is always there to speed the rebels to safety. Her amazing piloting and shooting skills make her a formidable enemy. But to her friends, Hera is a comforting presence—always willing to listen or give advice when her rebel shipmates need it.

Although Hera tries to be practical in most situations, she is an optimistic dreamer when it comes to the rebel cause. She truly believes that one day the small band of rebels will defeat the Empire. Anything she can do to make that dream a reality is an acceptable risk.

Hera and Kanan make the perfect team.

Sabine Wren

Sabine "fixes" a few Imperial posters.

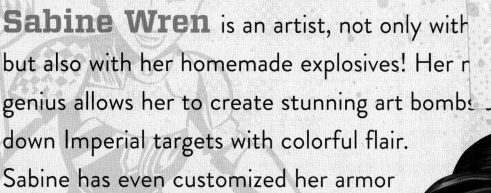

Sabine Wren is an artist, not only with [...] but also with her homemade explosives! Her r[...] genius allows her to create stunning art bomb[...] down Imperial targets with colorful flair. Sabine has even customized her armor and weapons with her own original designs.

Free-spirited and independent, Sabine will volunteer for any mission: the more dangerous and exciting, the better. If the rebels need someone to create a distraction, Sabine is the perfect person to do it—with style.

This grumpy astromech droid's real designation is C1-10P, but everyone just calls him **Chopper**. Chopper's cranky attitude sometimes drives the other rebels crazy, but they keep the droid around, since he's the only one who can keep the *Ghost* up and running.

Chopper's idea of a good time is pulling off a perfect prank. When Ezra joined the crew, he became the victim of most of the little droid's schemes. Deep down, though, he knows the droid is just having fun. When real trouble finds them, Chopper always comes through for the rebels—even if he complains the whole time!

No gravity is no problem for Chopper!

The rebels plan a mission in the *Ghost*'s cockpit.

The *Ghost*

is more than just the rebels' ship; it's their home. The midsize freighter might have a few dings and dents, but it's gotten the rebels out of plenty of close calls with the Empire. The ship also has lots of nooks and crannies where the rebels can hide smuggled items.

When they're not blasting TIE fighters from the gun turret beneath the bridge, the crew can be found relaxing in the ship's common room with a good game of holochess. The *Ghost* is equipped with a second, smaller ship—the *Phantom*—which the crew can use for stealth missions. No matter the challenge, the *Ghost* has the tech and the speed to get the job done.

Zare

Zare grew up on the planet of Uquine. Instead of picking pockets and collecting stormtrooper helmets like some kids, he went to the Imperial Academy just like his older sister, Dhara. When Zare's sister suddenly went missing, Zare realized that the Empire might be to blame. He hopes to one day find his lost sister.

Don't trust **Vizago**! Even though the rebels often buy information from this shady gangster, they know he he is really only out for himself. Still, doing small jobs for Vizago helps the rebels pay for the supplies they need. Plus, Vizago's intel has helped the rebels pull off more than one dangerous mission. As long as the Empire dominates the galaxy, the rebels will have to rely on gangsters like Vizago as the lesser of two evils.

Vizago

Aresko & Grint

Commandant Aresko and **Taskmaster Grint** are two Imperial officers who make life miserable for the people of Lothal.

Aresko's and Grint's clumsy attempts to catch Kanan's crew are easily foiled by the rebels, but for the unarmed, untrained people of Lothal, avoiding the officers' cruelty is much more difficult. That's why the rebels take every chance they can to pull one over on their foes.

Wookiees like **Wullffwarro** and **Kitwarr** know all too well the evils of the Galactic Empire.

Wullffwarro was a great chief among his people before he and his son Kitwarr were taken by the Empire and made to work in the spice mines of Kessel. The underground mines can be a death sentence for Wookiees who are used to open forests. Fortunately, they were rescued by the rebels and are now powerful allies on the side of the Rebellion.

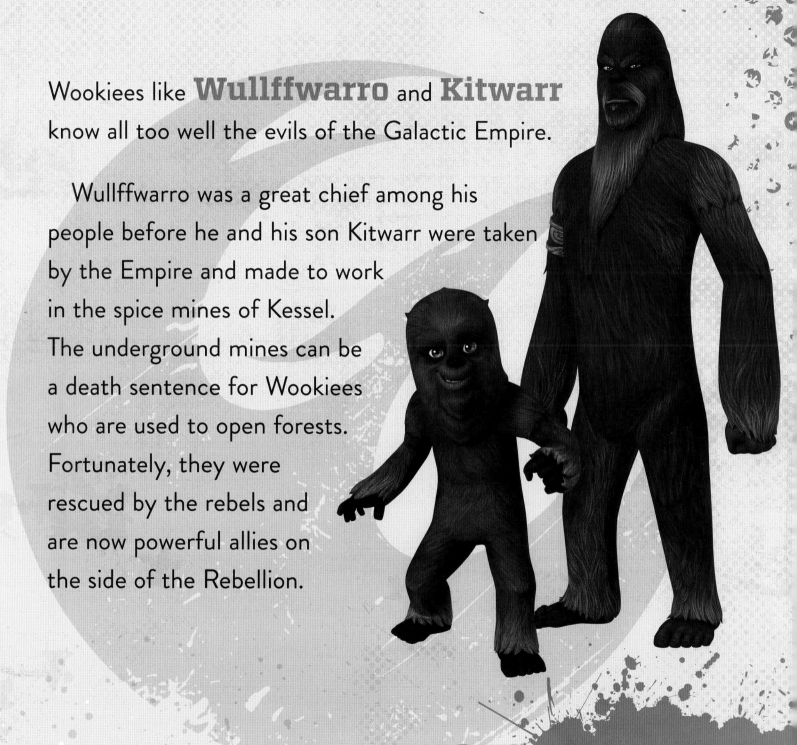

Wullffwarro & Kitwarr

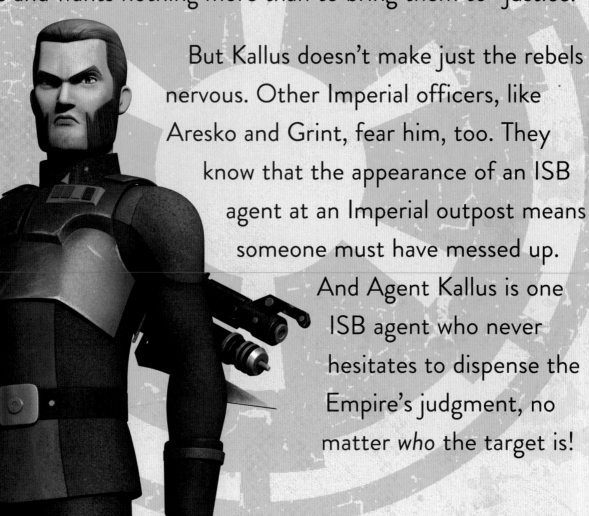

Agent Kallus is a member of the ISB—the Imperial Security Bureau. His mission is to seek out and destroy anyone disloyal to the Empire. Naturally, Kallus hates the rebels and wants nothing more than to bring them to "justice."

But Kallus doesn't make just the rebels nervous. Other Imperial officers, like Aresko and Grint, fear him, too. They know that the appearance of an ISB agent at an Imperial outpost means someone must have messed up. And Agent Kallus is one ISB agent who never hesitates to dispense the Empire's judgment, no matter *who* the target is!

Kallus orders his men to fire on the rebels.

When news of Kanan the rebel Jedi reached the Empire, the Inquisitor was sent to "deal" with the problem. **The Inquisitor's** job is to hunt down any surviving Jedi, and he is perfectly suited for the task. Being Force-sensitive, he is able to sense things before they happen and react with lightning-fast reflexes. This, along with his coldly logical mind, allows him to always keep a few steps ahead of his prey.

The Inquisitor carries a special lightsaber. It has two glowing red blades and a round hilt so that the lightsaber can rotate.

The Inquisitor checks in with Agent Kallus.

Stormtroopers

Stormtroopers are the infantry of the Galactic Empire. Wearing protective white armor and faceless helmets, they enforce Imperial law and maintain order throughout the galaxy. Regular men and women can be trained to become stormtroopers, though the rebels would caution against it. They know that the stormtroopers are used by the Empire to take over worlds and destroy freedom.

The rebels do all they can to stop the stormtroopers . . . and maybe, in Ezra's case, collect a few of their helmets along the way!